DIEGO RIVERA

Coloring Book

The *Detroit Industry* fresco cycle is a series of murals painted by Mexican muralist Diego Rivera (1886–1957) as a tribute to the workers in manufacturing, the sciences, and agriculture of Detroit, Michigan, in the 1930s. Rivera completed the twenty-seven-panel work in eleven months, from April 1932 to March 1933. The fresco cycle spans four walls in Detroit Institute of Arts. It is considered the finest example of Mexican mural art in the United States, and the artist thought it the best work of his career.

Rivera was a Marxist who believed that art belonged on public walls rather than in private galleries. He found his medium in the fresco, where paint is applied to wet plaster. Its vast size allowed him to explore grand and complex themes, which would be accessible to a large audience. In Mexico, Rivera's murals tied modern Mexican culture to its indigenous roots, revealing the ancient Indian cultures as Mexico's true heritage. Similarly, Rivera's *Detroit Industry* murals depict industry and technology as the indigenous culture of Detroit.

DETROIT
INSTITUTE
OF ARTS

AGES 3 to 103!

All drawings are based on details of *Detroit Industry*, a series of four frescos painted by Diego Rivera (Mexican, 1886–1957) and in the collection of Detroit Institute of Arts.

1. *Production and Manufacture of Engine and Transmission*, north wall automotive panel, detail (bottom center)

2. *Vaccination*, north wall, detail

3. *Michigan Fruits and Vegetables*, east wall, detail

4. *Manufacture of Poisonous Gas Bombs*, north wall, detail

5. *Production and Manufacture of Engine and Transmission*, north wall automotive panel, detail (bottom left)

6. *Vaccination*, north wall, detail

7. *Production and Manufacture of Engine and Transmission*, north wall automotive panel, detail (bottom right)

8. *Aviation*, west wall, detail

9. *The Predatory Hawk*, west wall

10. *Production and Manufacture of Engine and Transmission*, north wall automotive panel, detail (left of center)

11. *Steam and Electricity*, west wall, detail

12. *Pharmaceutics*, south wall, detail

13. *Production of Automobile Exterior and Final Assembly*, south wall automotive panel, detail (top center)

14. *Production of Automobile Exterior and Final Assembly*, south wall automotive panel, detail (bottom center)

15. *Production of Automobile Exterior and Final Assembly*, south wall automotive panel, detail (left of bottom center)

16. *The Peaceful Dove*, west wall

17. *Pharmaceutics*, south wall, detail

18. *Pharmaceutics*, south wall, detail

19. *Production of Automobile Exterior and Final Assembly*, south wall automotive panel, detail (bottom left)

20. *Commercial Chemical Operations*, south wall, detail

Pomegranate Communications, Inc.
19018 NE Portal Way, Portland OR 97230
800 227 1428   www.pomegranate.com

Color reproductions © 2015 Detroit Institute of Arts
Photographs are by Dirk Bakker and R. H. Hensleigh,
Detroit Institute of Arts.
Line drawings © Pomegranate Communications, Inc.

Item No. CB169

Designed by Tristen Jackman. Line drawings by Becky Holtzman.

Printed in Korea

24 23 22 21 20 19 18 17 16 15   10 9 8 7 6 5 4 3 2 1

Distributed by Pomegranate Europe Ltd.
Unit 1, Heathcote Business Centre, Hurlbutt Road
Warwick, Warwickshire CV34 6TD, UK
[+44] 0 1926 430111
sales@pomeurope.co.uk

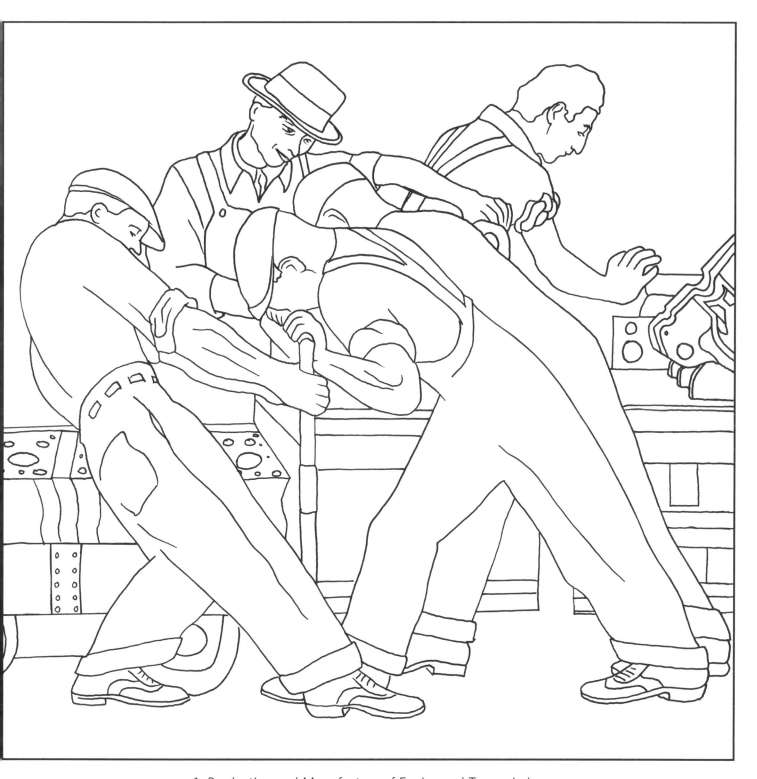

1. Production and Manufacture of Engine and Transmission

2. *Vaccination*

3. Michigan Fruits and Vegetables

4. [Manufacture of Chemical Gas]

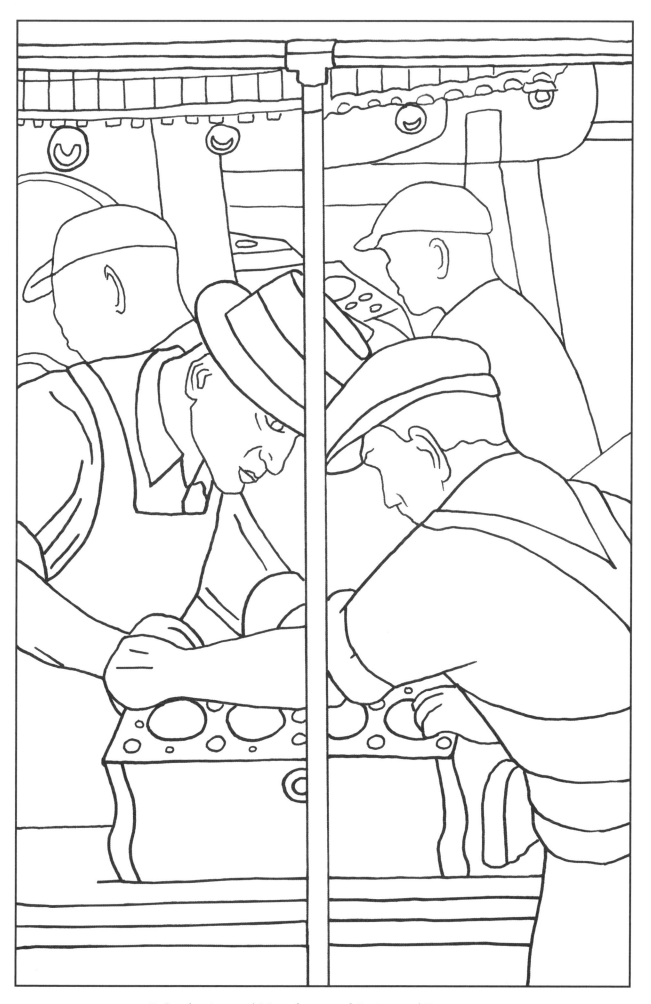

5. *Production and Manufacture of Engine and Transmission*

6. *Vaccination*

7. Production and Manufacture of Engine and Transmission

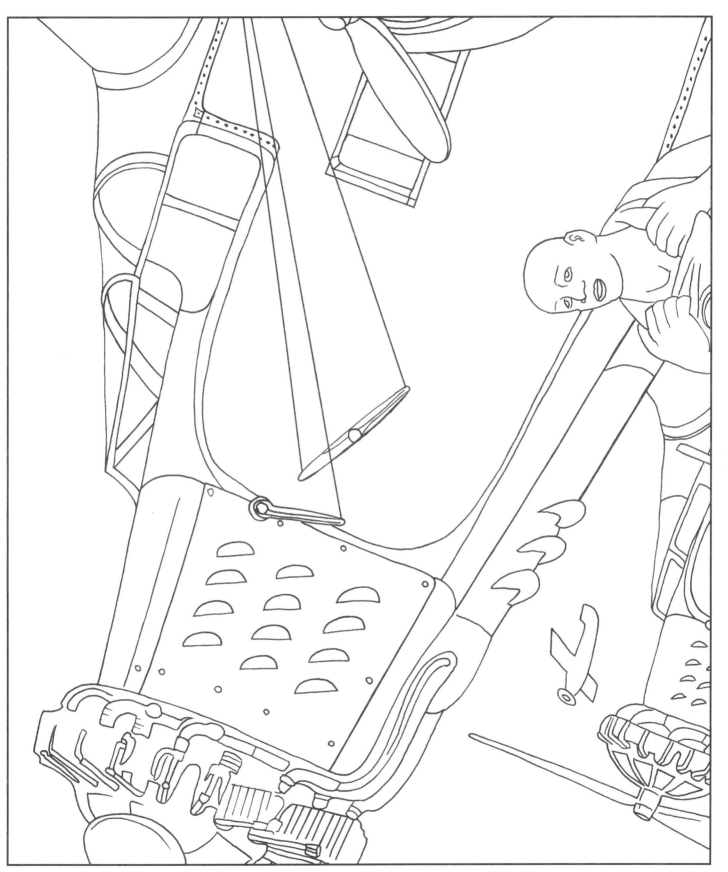

9. The Predatory Hawk

10. *Production and Manufacture of Engine and Transmission*

11. Steam

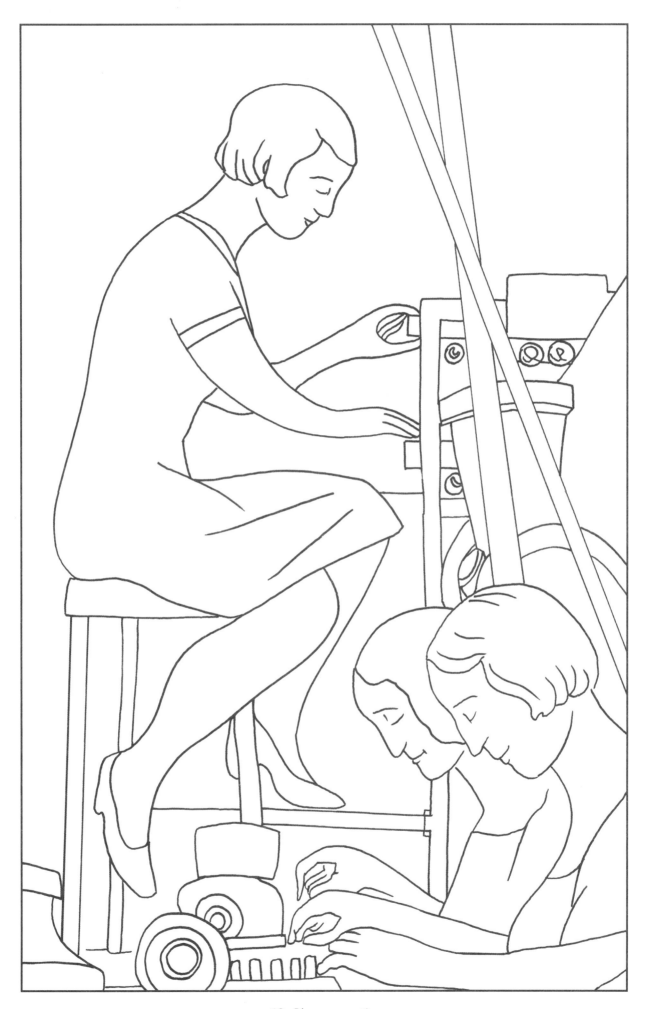

12. Pharmaceutics

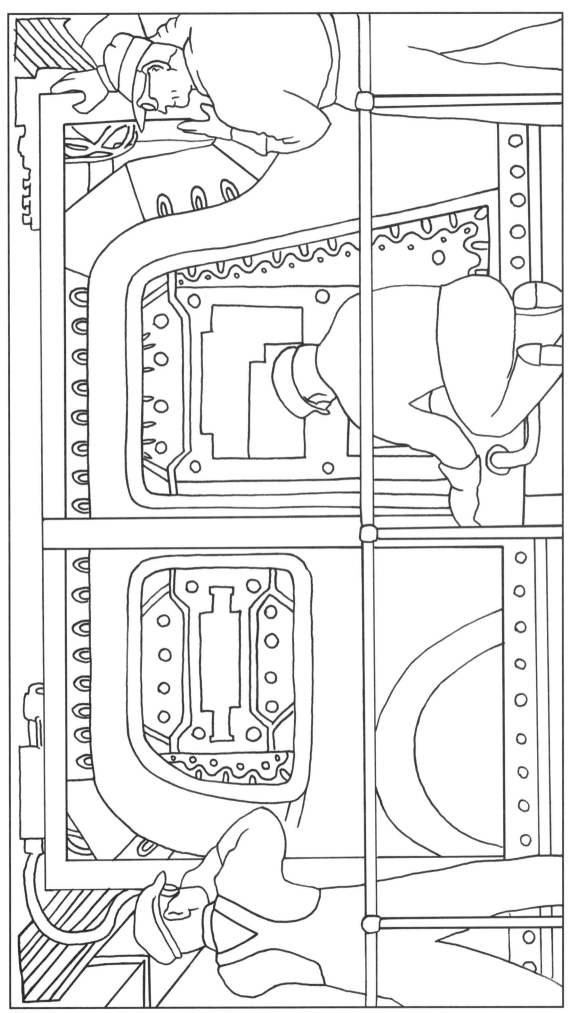

13. Production of Automobile Exterior and Final Assembly

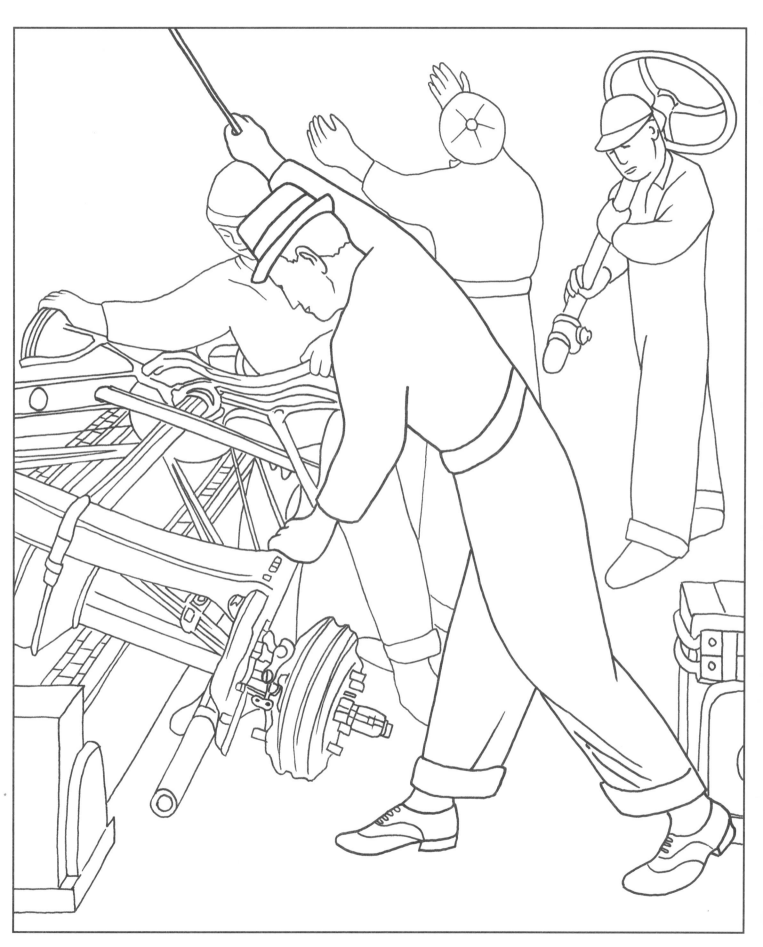

14. *Production of Automobile Exterior and Final Assembly*

15. *Production of Automobile Exterior and Final Assembly*

16. The Peaceful Dove

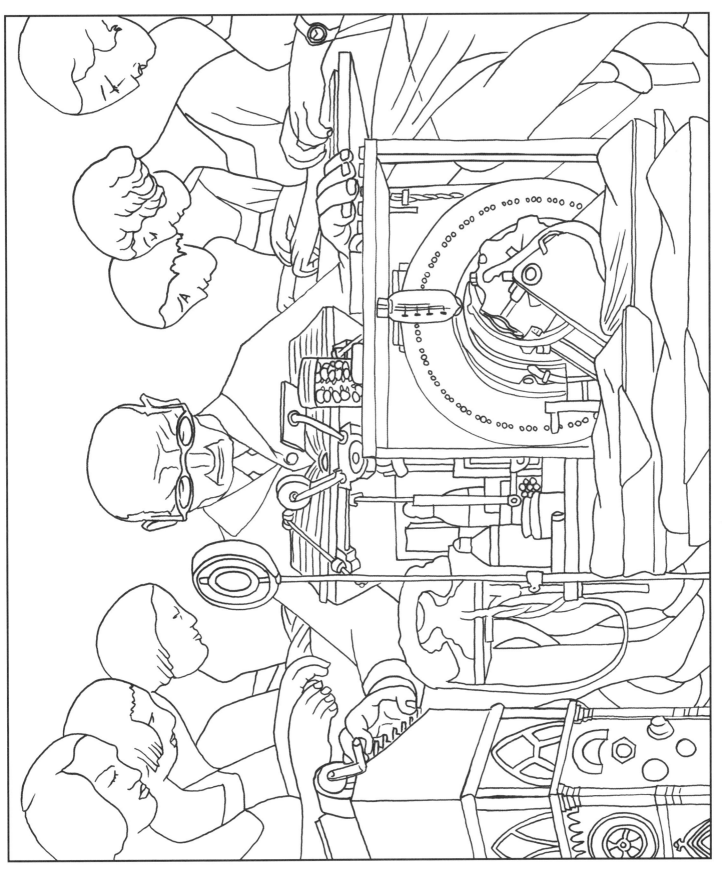

17. Pharmaceutics

18. *Pharmaceutics*

19. *Production of Automobile Exterior and Final Assembly*

20. *Commercial Chemical Operations*

Draw and color your own picture here!

Draw and color your own picture here!

Draw and color your own picture here!